HERBS FOR TODAY AND TOMORROW

JOAN RYDER

CONTENTS:

ACKNOWLEDGEMENTS

Sincere thanks are expressed to the following, whose advice and help in the preparation of this book have been greatly appreciated:-

MR. F. J. REED F.L.S. OF REDBOURN.

MR. B. J. STYLES OF
MESSRS. WILLIAM RANSOM AND SON, HITCHIN.

MISS A. MICKLETHWAITE OF ST. ALBANS.

MR. FREDERICK DAY OF DORKING.

MR. S. F. MAYES OF WOOLACOMBE,
AND MISS JOAN PAGE OF CROCKHAM HILL.

INTRODUCTION

The purpose of this book is to give to the reader some interesting information about some of our best known useful herbs. In response to many requests I have described the appearance and uses of a number of our British herbs so that those who love nature may recognise these 'friends of the field and hedgerow' and learn more about their virtues.

I wish to make one point very clear to all those who may care to read the notes on remedial uses of herbs. When we are not well we should at once consult our doctor, who is the right person to advise us. Herbs can also be used to improve and to maintain good health. Just as the housewife adds plenty of fresh vegetable salads and fruit to the family diet for the sake of their health, so the keen herbalist keeps at hand the appropriate plants to give as an added treatment in case of need.

Doctors include many herbs in their prescriptions, and research is continually going on to find new ways in which plants can be used to combat disease. Many synthetic preparations are made in these days which – so to speak – imitate the herbal preparation, but the herbalist is one who prefers, where possible, to use the actual plants themselves although they may perhaps be slower and more gentle in their effect. There is only room in this small book to mention a few of our wild plants, but I hope that readers – especially younger people – may be interested and may find pleasure in the study of nature.

Joan Ryder

HOW A PLANT GROWS

'Good growing weather' we say when the air is warm, the soil moist and leaf and flower begin to grace the hedgerows, gardens and farms. The annual miracle of growth, retarded when winds are cold, but re-asserting itself with the coming of spring, is too often taken for granted. When a seed is sown we expect a plant to appear as a tender shoot pushing its way through the brown earth, but we seldom marvel at the mystery of it all.

A seed is alive and consists of an outer coat enclosing a store of food and, in miniature, the beginning of the plant it will produce. Until warmth, air and moisture are sufficient it remains, as it were, inanimate; but a combination of these growth producers commences a chain of complex changes until the seed coat is broken by the new plant.

This is known as germination, and as the young shoot grows upward to the light, another thrusts itself down into the soil to form the first root. In these early days the seedling relies on its own food store, but soon root hairs, no more than one cell thick, grow from the roots. These are the foragers for food below ground and they absorb plant foods in solution in a most remarkable way. Inside the cells of the root hairs is a fluid, the concentration of which is usually far stronger than the solution of plant foods in the soil. The strong solution attracts the weak through the cell walls and then passes on the food to help the young plant in its struggle for survival. Gardeners know that if fertilizers are applied too liberally, plants will collapse. The reason for this is that the plant food concentration is made too high by the fertilizer and with the stronger solution in the soil the process is reversed. Fluids inside the plant are attracted out through the cell walls.

When the young shoot breaks through the soil it produces green leaves, which during daylight hours absorb air. Carbon dioxide is retained and oxygen liberated. Inside the plant carbon dioxide is converted into carbohydrates which make a valuable reserve of food. At one time an Orchid could not be grown from seed unless seeds were sown in a pot where an Orchid plant was growing. All attempts to sow in the normal way failed, no matter what compost was used. We now know that attached to the roots of Orchids is a fungus which lives as a parasite, robbing the growing plant of food. But when a young seedling is produced, the fungus makes contact with its meagre root system and feeds the young plant until it is strong enough to provide enough food for both.

Rate of growth varies considerably according to the type of plant, and light plays a very important part in growth and development. A green plant growing in darkness or subdued light does not normally become stunted. Indeed the reverse is true for it makes far greater progress than a plant growing in full light. The effect of light is to control growth.

Growth is brought about by cell multiplication at the tip of the shoot or growing point. Highly active cells multiply and as their numbers increase, so the plant grows. Chains of genes are known by botanists as chromosomes and these carry the characteristics of the plant. A species with a normal complement of sixteen chromosomes has that number in all its growing cells. When one cell divides to form two, the chromosomes split and temporarily there are thirty-two, but they then form two groups, each of sixteen. A cell wall forms between them and new cells are created.

If by accident the growing point is removed from a plant or it is pinched out by a gardener, side branches which before have been less active, take over the role and growth is maintained. Gardeners often treat plants in this way, so that instead of one tall stem there will be a number of sturdy growing side shoots which make the plant 'bushy'.

There is constant activity inside a living plant and tremendous energy is produced. A humble weed growing on a hard path has often broken through a rock-like surface with what would seem a tender shoot. Tree roots can disturb the foundations of houses, water weeds will overcome the flow of water until streams are diverted from their normal course. Their growth is rapid and it is a sobering thought, that what we know as Canadian Waterweed and which now fills so many of our lakes, ponds and streams is not a native of the British Isles. A few small pieces were originally imported. Now the weed is everywhere.

Plant growth, because it is happening all the time, fails to capture the imagination in the same way as less complex jet or piston engines. Man, with all his ingenuity, has produced nothing to equal this miracle of nature.

Herbs may seed themselves in many unusual places

NATURE'S MEDICINES *(From field to final product)*

Tremendous advances have been made in science since the beginning of this century. We have seen the introduction of many new synthetic medicines. Nevertheless, it is a significant fact that natural medicines obtained from vegetable medicinal plants still play an enormous part in the treatment of human suffering and illness.

Important plants grown on our English herb farms are Belladonna, Henbane, Stramonium, Foxglove, Colchicum, Chamomile, Peppermint and many others.

While many such medicinal plants are used in herbal remedies in their natural dried form, such as leaves, roots, barks, flowers and seeds, the use in the natural form by the medical profession is largely giving place to more scientific products made from them, such as extracts, tinctures, infusions, decoctions, distilled oils, tablets, and capsules.

How are these modern finished galenicals prepared today and what skill goes into their production? The story is a fascinating one. First, there is the careful selection of the correct strains of the plants for cultivation. Then there are the techniques of cultivation and the correct harvesting of the crops. All these call for the expert skill and long experience of horticulturists, botanists, chemists and other scientists.

After the crop is collected from the fields it is sent immediately to modern laboratories where it is dried in large drying rooms at a temperature below 140°F. This is done so that, as in the case of Belladonna leaves, the green colour and natural medicinal constituents can be retained in the dried plants. Drying is an important part of medicinal plant processing because, if the plants were kept for long in their natural fresh state after harvesting, certain ferments in them would destroy the active constituents on which the curative properties of the plant depend.

Plants dried in this way now become the raw materials from which galenicals such as extracts, tinctures, infusions, decoctions, etc., are made. Basically, galenical manufacture involves the maceration and percolation of the dried plants in solvents, i.e. solutions such as water or spirit, so that the active constituents of the plants are extracted.

Galenicals processed in this way are supplied to the pharmaceutical industry and thence to doctors and hospitals in the form of liquid extracts, tinctures, etc., of varying strength. Others are supplied in the form of soft semi-solid extracts, while yet others are presented as completely dry-solid extracts, and compressed tablets.

Another important way of extracting the valuable part of medicinal plants is by distillation. This process is used for the extraction of essential oils in such plants as Peppermint, Lavender, Chamomile, Dill, Aniseed, etc., where

Camomile growing on a herb farm

the oils exist in different parts of the plants. Briefly, the process involves the heating of the dried plants in large-scale stills containing water and other solvents, which are boiled and distilled. The steam from the process extracts the essential oils from the plants in the form of vapour, which together with the steam, is condensed in special equipment.

The processes outlined briefly above for extracting the natural medicinal constituents of the plants are by no means the end of the manufacture of the galenicals. A vital part of the processing is what is known as chemical assaying or standardization of the finished galenical.

It will readily be appreciated that there is some degree of difference in the amounts of active constituents of plants of the same species due to variations in different strains of the plants, of the soil in which they are grown and, to a certain extent, of the climatic conditions under which they were cultivated. As some of the constituents of many medicinal plants are powerful substances, it is necessary that the galenicals made from them are produced to a fixed known strength so that the products can be given in cases of illness in very accurate dosages. Thus, during the manufacture of the galenicals, expert chemists and analysts examine the products to test the amount of active constituents in them, and where necessary, make certain adjustments to the final product so that it conforms to fixed standards set by different countries of the world.

There are firms in England who have been specializing in this industry for over a century. During this time they have become perfectionists in every branch, from growing the plants on their farms to the final preparation of the standardized galenical. They have also evolved elaborate manufacturing equipment for carrying out their highly specialized art.

It is interesting to note that the term 'galenicals' comes from the name Galen (Galenos) who lived from A.D. 131 to 200 and listed many plants with their medicinal uses in his writings.

HERBS AND THEIR USES FOR
COMMON AILMENTS

ANAEMIA

Serious ill health may develop from a slight anaemic condition, and it is most important to deal promptly in such cases. Many anaemic people put off seeking the doctor's advice because they think that they are just tired and will feel better after a holiday, whereas definite treatment is necessary. They try to ignore the feelings of faintness or giddiness, breathlessness and poor appetite, hoping that these will pass off without medical assistance. It should be remembered that many children, especially young schoolgirls, become anaemic without this being noticed by parents and teachers, and the condition should be realised and dealt with in its early stages.

Plenty of rest should be taken every day and fresh air and sunshine enjoyed as much as possible. Every possible moment should be spent out of doors and stuffy rooms should be avoided.

Fresh vegetables, salads and fruit are most helpful. Of all the fresh vegetables available, spinach is the best for anaemic people. Wherever there is garden space make frequent sowings of Perpetual Spinach and serve as often as possible. When children dislike this vegetable, it can be served in different and attractive ways instead of being put in a wet lump on the plate!

Many herbs contain valuable juices to assist recovery from anaemia. One of the best is Holy Thistle (Carduus Benedictus). This can be taken blended with Wood Sage and other suitable herbs in a compound herb tea. Plants particularly recommended are Liquorice (root), Balm, Burdock, Red Clover and Hops.

ARTHRITIS

Those who are suffering from arthritis, and who are receiving special medical treatment for this complaint, often enquire whether there are any herbs which will benefit them, as they wish to use herbs in addition to help improve their condition.

Several herbs are helpful in these cases: two particularly effective ones being Yarrow (Achillea Millefolium) and Guaiacum (Lignum vitae). These, blended with other herbs which are laxative and some which soothe pain, should be taken in the form of herb tea every day. The bark and leaves of the common Ash tree (Fraxinus excelsior) are remedial in their action, and Ash Leaf pills taken daily give considerable help in cases of arthritis and gout.

It is most necessary to eat good nourishing food. Rheumatism and arthritis develop quickly where the body is run down and under-nourished. Many mothers and housewives who sacrificed their rations for the children during the war became rheumatic due to lack of essential foods. Should a sufferer from these complaints feel unlike eating at the proper meal time, tempting 'snacks' will sometimes appeal at a different hour. 'It doesn't matter when they eat as long as they EAT', says one famous rheumatism specialist.

Yarrow

CHEST COMPLAINTS

Chest sufferers need herbs. First and foremost, they should take regularly an infusion to help the respiratory passages. Those who suffer from bronchitis during the winter months should take chest herbs in October and continue while cold winds or fogs prevail.

An important herb for the chest is Comfrey, (Symphytum officinale). It has a soothing and healing action. It is blended with other herbs such as Liquorice root, Horehound and Linseed to make a tea.

For a cough, herbs that are soothing and slightly expectorant should be used. Elecampane, Pleurisy Root and Squills are recommended.

At night, keep a steaming vessel near the bed with some Friar's Balsam in hot water. In the case of a baby or young child wearied with coughing this simple method will soon ease the breathing and stop the cough. The boiling kettle or saucepan should be in a very safe place in the child's bedroom to guard against every possible chance of an accident.

Children who are prone to asthma need to be given a sense of complete security and freedom from any fears, such as the dread of failing an examination.

An excellent herb to help in cases of asthma is Datura Stramonium (Thorn Apple). Although this herb is on the poison list it is beneficial when inhaled and therefore it is permitted to be incorporated in herbal cigarettes which are recommended for sufferers from asthma.

THE COMMON COLD

What a lot of valuable working hours and days at school are lost through the common cold, that well-known enemy which attacks us so often, and particularly during the English winter.

Let us say first of all that, as a rule, not enough wise precautions are taken against catching cold. Busy people allow themselves to get run down and badly overtired and then they are an easy prey when colds are about and the east wind is blowing.

Before the bad weather begins these people should take a good herb tonic, more rest, and plenty of nourishing food. They can then set out in the most treacherous weather feeling strong and not thinking about colds or influenza. Should they encounter any infection, they will be in good health and better able to throw it off. Light but warm (pure wool) clothing is essential, and the feet must be kept warm and dry.

When anyone feels that they have caught a chill and experience shivering and other warning symptoms, there is an excellent herbal remedy which should be taken immediately. This is a mixture of Elderflower and Peppermint which is an old-fashioned remedy for colds but, like many old-fashioned remedies, is thoroughly reliable and effective. It should always be kept handy.

The infusion should be taken in hot water, or if preferred in hot milk, as soon as a cold is suspected. A glass taken when in bed is especially good.

An interesting experience has recently been related by a mother of three young children. All three were subject to very heavy running colds and missed weeks of school during bad weather, thus making very little progress with lessons and being well behind others of their age. One of the children, being a bronchial subject, always had an extra week or two in bed with bronchitis after each of the heavy colds and became very run down and thin.

On the advice of a friend, the mother kept at hand the mixture of Elderflower and Peppermint, giving this immediately to the children at the first sign of a cold. Since that day their colds have been thrown off in a couple of days. The bronchial child was given an infusion of chest herbs daily from October onwards and bronchitis has not followed the slight cold any more. The general health of the children has also greatly improved and school attendance has been regular.

Those suffering from influenza will be well advised to take these herbs from time to time during the day and last thing at night, as they restore warmth to the body and give a pleasant 'glow' which relieves the discomfort felt during flu attacks. They induce gentle perspiration and the patient should keep well wrapped up. Children should be watched in case they throw off the bedclothes during sleep.

When one hears the remark 'No one can do anything for the common cold', one is tempted to enquire whether herbs have been given a fair trial, and have been kept in the house ready for prompt use.

HERBS FOR THE HAIR

One of the first signs of ill health is often lifeless and thinning hair, and everyone wishing to avoid this should keep fit with a good herb tonic and, if necessary, some herbs for the nerves. Undue strain, worry and fatigue soon cause the hair to be out of condition and it becomes dull and lifeless, losing its natural gloss.

While taking care to build up general health, give the hair, at the same time, a good course of herbal treatment.

The best of all herbs known for this purpose is Rosemary (Rosmarinus officinalis), which stimulates the scalp and enlivens the hair after only a few applications. In the days of the first Queen Elizabeth, the ladies used to throw sprigs of fresh Rosemary into the water when they washed their hair to prevent it from going grey and to make it ready for the magnificent coiffures that were worn in those days. It is delightful to look at the portraits of the first Elizabethan ladies and to see the glorious appearance of their hair, built up high on the head and finished with ropes of pearls. Hair that was dull and lifeless would have spoiled the whole appearance just as it does with our freer hair styles today. No permanent wave or modern hair style looks well if the texture of the hair is poor.

Here are some of the ways in which herbs can help people who are worried about this matter.

For hair in poor condition shampoo with essence of Rosemary Shampoo, ready prepared for use. If the hair is seriously in need of a tonic and is falling out rapidly shampoo with the following herbs placed in a muslin bag and infused well into the hot water: Southernwood, Box leaves (Buxus Sempervirens), crushed Quillia and herbs for fragrance. In between these tonic shampoo treatments, massage extract of Rosemary into the scalp daily. This extract is excellent for greasy hair and any dandruff.

If the hair is particularly dry and lacking a natural healthy oiliness, massage

Rosemary

with a nourishing lotion which contains Oil of Rosemary, Quassia, Witch Hazel, Box leaves and Southernwood.

It will be noticed that after herbs have been used the hair not only improves in health but also becomes much more buoyant and can more easily be arranged in its own natural waves. Plenty of brushing is essential, especially after the Rosemary massage. Use pure bristle brushes and never drag at the hair or the head with harsh brushes or combs. Children tend to become very restless during a ten minute brush, so mothers will do well to have an interesting book or puzzle to hand to them to keep them occupied. Herb lotions followed by a long gentle brushing will ensure wonderful growth and appearance in children's hair. Avoid any scolding, and always encourage the children by praising their appearance and allowing them to choose their own hair styles.

It is necessary, while on this subject, to point out that where there has been severe nervous strain and fatigue, the person concerned may suffer from Alopecia. This causes the appearance of thin bald patches in various places on the head. The appearance of these patches is most depressing for the sufferer and the case should be dealt with by the doctor's advice directly it appears. If so advised, special treatment at the hairdressers should be arranged, and in the meantime, the patient should continue to build up the health and especially the nerves.

Opinions differ as to the advisability or otherwise of wearing a hat. Many of us feel that, as a rule, fresh air is a reliable tonic. There are few treatments better for the hair than to shampoo it with a herb shampoo on a warm day and allow it to dry out of doors, brushing it from time to time to allow the air and sun to reach all parts of the scalp.

INDIGESTION

These are days of rush and strain for almost everyone, and it is not long since we all went through the experience of a great war. It is not surprising, therefore, that many people suffer from indigestion. All kinds of causes contribute to this discomfort.

First of all, life is lived at too quick a pace. People rush to the train or the bus soon after a hurried meal, or after that meal they sit cooped up in the driving seat of a car for many hours without any change of position or any natural exercise and free breathing. How can the body carry out its proper digestive functions in such circumstances? We learn from those expert in these matters of health that the worst sufferers from indigestion are the transport workers. After a heavy and probably starchy meal, a driver sits in his vehicle for a long journey. Stomach discomfort is frequent and often more serious troubles, such as gastric ulcers, may develop.

Another form of indigestion experienced by many people is nervous indigestion. Worried and harassed by overwork, family cares, business responsibilities and so on, many people eat their meals hurriedly with their minds working hard at the problem of the moment. Food taken in this way will never be properly and comfortably assimilated. It is better not to eat anything at all than to eat it in this way! A quarrel at the dinner table between members of the family will cause a little child to be sick after eating even the most plain and suitable food. Older persons eating in an atmosphere of strain or hostility will also suffer later from digestive pains. How wise is the old Book of Proverbs when it reminds us 'better a dinner of herbs where love is, than a feast with strife'.

What can we do to put matters right from the start, rather than be forced constantly to take remedies to relieve the indigestion that should never have been there?

Obviously it is most difficult for a good many of us to change our jobs, but we can change our method of getting through these jobs. When rushing about, or driving for long hours, it is wise to eat very light but nourishing food and eat it sparingly. Plan to eat a heavier meal slowly and without thinking about work and worry. After such a meal rest quietly and later take a leisurely walk in the fresh air. Those continually travelling in car or train should make time when off duty for a walk amid fresh green surroundings. Sometimes it seems as though many of our people have forgotten how to walk and must go everywhere in some sort of vehicle!

Some need an antacid diet, others need to increase or reduce weight. Health foods today are playing a most important part in improving digestion and people are learning the great benefit they can obtain from fruit and vegetable juices and all the latest starch reduced foods. The Dandelion is a fine herb for the digestion and Dandelion coffee should be taken as often as possible. This coffee has a delicate and delightful flavour and is a tonic. It is made from the pure roasted Dandelion root.

Let us remember how herbs were used with foods in the olden days to help digestion. Greasy foods, such as goose, duck and pork, were always served with stuffings, such as sage and onion. These herbs counteract the richness of the dish and ensure that it will not prove too fatty, Parsley, Mint, Thyme, and all the favourite culinary herbs have similar useful action and the more they are used in our cooking the better. All the Mints are good as digestives, the best known being the Peppermint which can be taken in various forms. A cup of Mint tea will prove helpful in stomach disorders.

Those suffering with nervous indigestion due to worry and strain should take an infusion of herbs that will be both easing to the digestion and soothing for the nerves. In addition to Dandelion, Gentian and Fennel, Scullcap and Valerian may be added for this purpose. Herbs that are aperient in their action can be included in the compound, and the most frequently used for this purpose is Senna. All those who tend to suffer from these troubles need to guard against constipation by the right diet and herb laxatives from time to time.

Slippery Elm bark powdered and made into a food is a wonderful healer in cases of stomach trouble. It has soothing properties and acts as an 'internal poultice'. It relieves stomach pain. Those travelling, driving long distances, and working away from home, can take the bark of this miraculous tree in tablet form. A tablet should be taken a little while before eating or drinking, and another can be taken after food. Many a delicate baby's life has been saved by Slippery Elm food when every other kind of feeding has failed.

One final word! Instead of having to think how to cure indigestion, let us concentrate on not having it!

Rhyming Advice
Eat slowly! Only men in rags
And gluttons, old in sin,
Mistake themselves for carpet bags
And pour the vittles in.

THE KIDNEYS

The action of the kidneys is most important for health, as they eliminate waste matter from the system. Bladder discomforts, backaches, and other symptoms of kidney disorders, should be dealt with immediately.

Herbs can be of great assistance and may be used in conjunction with any medical treatment that is advised. Most people think at once of drinking lemon barley water, and do not perhaps realise that certain herbs are particularly effective in cases of kidney trouble. An infusion of Clivers, Wild Carrot, Juniper berries, and other English herbs of similar action, will be found most helpful, while Parsley Piert is invaluable for dissolving stones and gravel and will often help the most obstinate cases.

A useful foreign herb called Buchu (Barosma Betulina) is the best known herb for the relief of cystitis. When there is any bladder inflammation, uncomfortable burning sensations, or catarrh of the bladder, Buchu will be found wonderfully helpful. No English herb quite equals it for these purposes, and when, during the last war, it was difficult to import supplies from Africa, herbalists were greatly handicapped when advising treatment. The leaves of the plant are used as they contain a remedial volatile oil.

Plenty of fruit juices and vegetable juices should be taken to benefit the kidneys, and also Dandelion coffee. A doctor's advice on diet should always be sought, as it is usual to reduce the intake of proteins when suffering from any kidney disorder.

THE LIVER

People who become 'liverish' from time to time know only too well how very depressing these attacks can be. The liver is a most important organ in the body and when out of order causes sickness, giddiness, headaches and general discomfort.

Among the herbs which will be found helpful are Wild Carrot, Dandelion, Liverwort and Agrimony. The herb 'Liverwort', of course, speaks for itself by its own old name. It is an English plant (Peltigera canina) and is particularly effective when blended with other herbs.

Those who are subject to liverish attacks should remember to take a short course of liver herbs occasionally, as by this means they may be able to prevent recurrence of the trouble. People who wake up in the morning feeling heavy and out of sorts, with no proper appetite for a good breakfast, would be well advised to take some liver herbs at night before retiring. The old-fashioned phrase 'you must have got out of the wrong side of the bed this morning' often indicates that the person addressed may be feeling the effects of a liver attack. Herbal treatment will help us to get out of bed on the *right* side!

MATERNITY

In these days special attention is paid to the health and well-being of the expectant mother, and she is given expert advice on diet and routine and is also shown how to practise relaxation in order that the arrival of the baby may be as easy as possible.

All this is good and the mother-to-be should avail herself of every possible aid to easier childbirth.

However, the experienced herbalist maintains that NOTHING can take the

Raspberry

place of the ideal herb for the expectant mother, namely the Raspberry (Rubus Idaeus). This acts beneficially on the essential organs.

Some expectant mothers prefer to take Raspberry leaves in tablet form, but as plenty of liquid is always advised during pregnancy, the herb tea is undoubtedly best and is good for the kidneys, which is important at this time.

Throughout many years those interested in the subject have noted the splendid effects of taking these herbs during pregnancy. Regular doses of Raspberry leaf tea not only keep the mother-to-be in good health and feeling comfortable during the waiting time, they also ensure a short confinement. Whereas the hours of confinement (especially with the first baby) might be very long; after a regular course of the herb tea during the last five months, the time of the actual birth is considerably shortened.

A typical example is given in this extract from a letter from a young mother telling of the arrival of her first baby. 'The nurse told me the baby would be many more hours coming, and I would probably have to wait until well on in the morning. She made a guess at about seven or eight o'clock a.m. and you can imagine I was very pleased when my little daughter arrived quickly and easily before midnight. I have been able to recommend Raspberry leaf tea to other expectant mothers, knowing from experience how much it will help them'.

Raspberry leaf tea is quite pleasant and easy to take and a wineglass dose should be taken several times a day. When the actual time of confinement begins, a cup of the tea taken warm will be found helpful.

MIGRAINE

It is with great sympathy that one hears of the pain suffered by those subject to attacks of this wretched trouble. Migraine is an obstinate and one might also say a mysterious complaint, so many and so varied are the apparent causes of an attack. It is most noticeable that the people who suffer from it most are often those who have exacting work and those carrying important responsibilities. They are, therefore, all the more inconvenienced by having to remain at home lying down when they would wish to be actively engaged in their duties. The case of one lady is typical: she is the secretary of a large organisation and every year she has to start preparing well in advance for an important annual conference. Round about the time of this International meeting a severe attack of migraine invariably occurs. It would seem that the strain and effort of preparation begins to tell on the system and then comes a collapse.

One lesson we can learn from these experiences is that the sufferer from this complaint must do some serious thinking about readjusting his or her life and work in order to find time for complete relaxation. If possible one should try to set aside an hour every day to lie down; relax the limbs and try to stop the mind from working! This is easier said than done, but a little practise does wonders. Some of us find that to listen quietly to music with the body relaxed and the eyes closed is a splendid way to ease up. Later, we are able to rise up feeling quite refreshed.

The advice of a doctor, and particularly of an experienced dietician, should be sought. The diet which helps to cause migraine seems to vary with different people. A case was reported of a schoolgirl whose attacks of migraine occurred every few weeks with most distressing hours of pain. A doctor suggested that all fruit should be discontinued as the patient was enormously fond of fruit and ate large quantities of all kinds, as well as many fresh salads. All these had to be given up and only one banana a week was allowed as a small treat! A very dull diet of milk puddings, wholemeal bread and so on was prescribed and in a very short time the attacks became milder and ceased. It would, therefore, seem worth while trying a different food programme from the one normally taken to see if benefit can be obtained.

Herbs can help the sufferer considerably, and herbs for the liver should be taken once or twice a week to ensure that it is working properly. Nerve herbs can be taken daily as these will help to prevent nervous tension and may well prevent the onset of an attack.

Children and young people who are subject to migraine may have an attack while worrying about an examination or when over-studying, or when the extra strain of starting in a new school has to be faced. Every effort should be made to reassure these young people and to help them to relax. Nerve herbs should be given daily as a precaution and can be given in pill form to avoid the necessity of drinking rather bitter liquid. Again, avoid acid and greasy foods, and use health foods and drinks as much as possible.

The best and safest nerve herbs for children are Scullcap and Mistletoe.

We must remember that peace of mind and confidence are essential. Careful thought should be given to the home situation where there is a migraine sufferer. The patient may be making efforts to control the feelings while constantly worried or irritated by some member of the family or the home circle. A complete change of environment has been tried in some cases, and has been followed by a decrease and then a cessation of the attacks.

Mistletoe

THE NERVES

It is sad indeed to note the increase in nervous troubles in these present times. World wars, with all their strain and stress, and the suffering they leave behind, have added disastrously to the number of people experiencing nervous disorders of one sort or another.

Some important points must be kept in mind. First, nervous disorders do not always appear at the time of the strain. Sometimes symptons develop after quite a long period has elapsed. Secondly, the physical health of the person concerned must be built up, as then nervous weakness can be more easily overcome. Plenty of nourishing food and rest, plenty of fresh air, change of scene and pleasant occupations, such as hobbies and outside interests, will all help. 'I used to be so lonely, and I used to brood over my health and wonder if I had an incurable complaint', writes one elderly lady, 'until I took on the job of helping at the Welfare Centre and now I don't have time to think about myself at all'. To be too much alone is never advisable, though times of quiet are necessary. We should remember the old motto, 'the best way to have friends is to be one'. There is a charming old saying about a happy man that 'His entrance into the room was as if another candle had been lighted'. It would be a better world if we all went about bringing more light into the places where we go.

Every person suffering in any way from nervous troubles should realise how tremendously herbs can help them. In addition to any special treatment already being given by the doctor, herbs should be taken daily. Gradually the patient will find that the strong drugs being taken as 'tranquillizers' can be reduced and the gentle and soothing effects of the herbs will be experienced.

The advice of the doctor must be sought in order to learn the real cause and nature of the nervous trouble, then the following suggestions may be useful.

For anxiety state, depression, inability to face up to one's daily duties and similar feelings, a compound herb tea should be taken frequently containing herbs known to be valuable 'nervines'. Mistletoe, Valerian, Vervain, Hops and other herbs can be used as advised.

For neuritis, neuralgia and other nerve pains, Mistletoe, Hops and Scullcap should also be taken. Sufferers from neural pains will find a course of Brewers Yeast Tablets particularly beneficial, as these contain Vitamin B.

For restlessness, insomnia and similar feeling where the sufferer cannot relax, the best herbs are some of the nervines mentioned above with Valerian and German Chamomile added. On going to bed or resting during the day, the patient should practise relaxing completely and loosening all the limbs and muscles. The head should rest on or near a pillow filled with herbs which induce restful sleep, such as Hops, Lavender and Rosemary.

Hysteria, over-excitability and nervous twitching will be greatly relieved by the simple herb known as Scullcap. This has been described by experts as 'one of the finest nervines ever discovered'. In fact, it is so excellent that its use can be recommended with the utmost confidence to any nerve sufferer. All these natural remedies are non-habit forming, simple to prepare and easy to take. They can be obtained in pill form.

The very latest form of herb tonic for nerves consists of a fine powder. This is the result of scientific methods of extracting the juices of the plants and then preparing them in a dried form. This produces a concentrated nerve remedy which is very quick in action and easy to take.

One final word. Nerve sufferers are really ill – not just 'being difficult'.

Valerian

One cannot see the outward sign of this illness, like a broken leg or bandaged wound but this invisible illness is none-the-less severe and hard to bear. Never tell nerve sufferers that they are to blame or that they ought to 'pull themselves together'. They cannot do this and scolding will do more harm than good. Help them to find outside interests and friends, encourage them to get the right advice and to persevere with every possible treatment until they improve. Nature means us all to be well and to enjoy life. We must believe in the Divine purpose for us which is HEALTH of body and mind.

PILES (HAEMORRHOIDS)

Many people would be spared a very trying operation if they would only resort to herbal treatment in the early stages of pile trouble. 'How many of our soldiers', wrote an officer in the last war, 'would have avoided a wretched time in hospital if they had only known about pile herbs! I shall never be without them so that I can supply anyone with treatment now that I am happily cured myself'.

This complaint may begin quite suddenly, perhaps due to constipation and the frequent use of strong purgatives. A gentle herbal laxative is always best, and it is not necessary to worry too much about constipation. Wise diet and a healthy routine with regular exercise will usually adjust matters.   Fruit and vegetables and plenty of suitable fluids such as fruit juices and vegetable extracts should be taken and heavy starchy foods avoided.

As soon as any discomfort from piles is felt, the sufferer will benefit from a herb tea containing Pilewort, Comfrey root and Witch Hazel. A glass of this tea drunk in the morning and occasionally at other times during the day will have an astringent action, thus reducing swelling. Smoothing the painful area with a herb ointment also containing Pilewort will prove most comforting. Suppositories of Pilewort and Witch Hazel can be inserted for internal healing. Piles often occur during pregnancy. Fortunately these are usually not too troublesome and herbal treatment soon clears them away.

Nature has provided for us the ideal means of relief in the simple plants which are well known and have been used throughout the centuries. We should value them highly and be grateful for the healing and comfort they bring.

PURIFYING THE BLOOD

Many of our wild plants are wonderfully effective for the purpose of purifying the blood, and it seems a great pity that they are not more widely recommended.

Herbs clear the system of impurities which cause skin eruptions and many uncomfortable symptoms. A herb tea for this purpose should be taken every spring and autumn and at other times as required. People with skin complaints, rashes, shingles, ulcerated places on the legs, chilblains and many other discomforts will benefit greatly by a course of purifying herbs, such as Echinacea, Burdock and Fumitory.

A wonderful experience was recorded by a German family. They lived in a cellar during the bombing of Berlin. When they emerged the daughter was suffering from terrible ulcers and boils. Amid the wreckage of their home they managed to find a packet of purifying herbs which had been lying there for some five years. The herbs were still effective and in a few days the tea began to improve the patient's condition; the skin began to clear, and the general health improved. 'In three weeks the results were little short of miraculous', wrote the girl's father.

RHEUMATISM

Research is constantly being carried out in an effort to find out more about the causes of rheumatism.

All those who suffer, even slightly, from rheumatic pains would be well advised to include a suitable herb tea in their daily diet.

Many herbs help rheumatic sufferers simply by clearing the system of impurities and thus removing the causes of trouble. As a general rule, an infusion of several herbs is the best form of treatment. Yarrow, Celery seed, Burdock and Uva ursi are excellent and the addition of Poplar bark (Populus tremula) has also been found beneficial.

At this present time a special method of preparing a herbal treatment for rheumatism is being perfected. The juices of the plants are being extracted and prepared in dried concentrated form. This promises to be a highly valuable contribution to the fight against rheumatism.

SOME BRITISH SIMPLE HERBS

AGRIMONY
(*Agrimonia Eupatoria*)

The leaves of this plant are rather dark green and are pointed at the tip. The 5 petalled flowers are yellow, and grow on long spikes. The plant blooms all the summer, growing to one foot high. It can be found in meadows and hedgerows.

This herb has been popular through the centuries to help digestion and to ease coughs. Today a small quantity is used with Raspberry leaves in tea for expectant mothers. It is found helpful in compounds for the stomach and liver.

ASH LEAVES (*Fraxinus excelsior*)

This is the common Ash – a fine tree which is seen in woods and gardens all over the country. It can be quickly recognised by its bark and leaves which are greyish in colour. The flowers appear on the branches in little clusters before the leaves. Branches of the tree put in water in the winter are a most attractive house decoration as they begin to flower. When the 'keys' develop, they flutter delightfully in the wind. The leaves, arranged in pairs along a stalk with one pointed leaf at the tip, number from seven to eleven.

Both the bark and leaves are used medicinally, but the most important service this tree renders is to relieve the pain of rheumatism and arthritis. The leaves, blended into a compound with other herbs or made into pills, have given wonderful comfort to sufferers from these complaints.

AVENS (*Geum urbanum*)

This plant is found in hedges or on the edge of woods and appears in May or June. It is about one foot tall and has a small yellow flower at the top of the stalk with five petals. The leaves are light green with toothed edges. Country people often know this plant by the name of Herb Bennet.

The action of the herb is astringent and it is sometimes used to relieve diarrhoea and to assist in checking certain weaknesses and forms of debility.

21

BLADDERWRACK *(Fucus Vesiculosus)*

Other names for this seaweed are Seawrack and Cutweed. It is found all round our coasts, having a long frond which is rather black in colour and bearing small round bladders in pairs. There are other seaweeds rather similar in appearance, therefore when trying to recognise the Vesiculosus, one must look for the pairs of bladders which identify the variety.

This plant is dried and often given in pill form as an aid to losing weight. It assists in removing surplus liquid from the body by helping to clear the kidneys. It is often prepared as a bath seaweed and placed in the bath water to benefit rheumatic sufferers. It is also known as Kelp, and contains natural salts, minerals, and iodine, which assist the bodily functions.

BLUE MALLOW *(Malva sylvestris)*

Otherwise known as the Common Mallow, this herb can be seen in many parts of England, on road-sides and waste ground. The flowers are deepish pink and sometimes almost red-purple, with five petals. The leaves are almost round in shape, covered with soft hairs, and the whole plant grows to about two feet in height. It flowers in the summer, making pleasant patches of colour, but it is a rather persistent and difficult weed to control. It has some medicinal value and has often been used as an infusion for colds and coughs.

BROOM *(Cytisus scoparius)*

Broom is found in Great Britain. It is about four feet high. The dark green sprays bear bright yellow flowers, singly or in pairs. These flowers are larger than Gorse, which they resemble, and are very popular for decoration. The seed pod is about two inches long and dark in colour.

In times past, Broom was esteemed for making a drink beneficial to nursing mothers, and the first Elizabethans considered it useful to counteract the ill-effects of unwise eating and drinking. It is seldom used today, but some herbalists still favour the use of Broom blended with Agrimony and Dandelion root for the relief of dropsy and for some liver troubles.

BUCKBEAN *(Menyanthes trifoliata)*

Buckbean or Marsh Trefoil, as it is sometimes called, grows in damp places and can be found beside streams or in watery meadows. It has a spike about six inches high which bears a number of white five-pointed flowers tinged at the edges with red. The roots are creeping and thickly matted. There are three leaves at the end of each leaf stalk. The flowers appear rather early in the summer in many parts of Britain.

Buckbean is used with other herbs as a blood purifier, and it is beneficial for skin complaints and rheumatism.

BUGLOSS *(Echium vulgare)*

This is sometimes called Viper's Bugloss and grows into a fine tall plant sometimes over two feet high. The leaves are narrow, pointed and covered with bristles. All the way up the spike are flowers which slowly change in colour during the season, varying from reddish purple to blue. Bugloss grows in many parts of Britain on waste places and rather dry ground, often showing to great advantage on the Sussex Downs. The best time to look for it is in July.

Its main use is for the relief of feverish conditions.

BURDOCK (*Arctium Lappa*)

Burdock is a very strong plant, growing up to five feet high. It has large leaves resembling rhubarb leaves, with white fibres underneath. The flowers are not very conspicuous, being a pinkish mauve and blooming at the end of long rather untidy sprays. When the flowers turn to seeds or, more correctly, to fruits, they form 'burs' which cling to the clothes and are quite difficult to remove. Burdock is found in hedgerows and woods in July and August.

Among all the herbs which are used for purifying the blood, Burdock is one of the most valuable. The root is used in conjunction with other herbs for this purpose. The fruits are used for kidney affections.

BURNET Greater (*Sanguisorba officinalis*)

This is a perennial herb which grows to about two feet in height. The foliage consists of sprays bearing nine or more leaves which are pointed round the edges, and it has a compact head of purple flowers. It is seen flowering in Scotland and in some parts of England during the summer. The garden plant, Salad Burnet, is cultivated for its pleasant taste in salads.

The Greater Burnet has special qualities as an astringent, and has been found useful in cases of bleeding piles. In olden times the plant was used for staunching wounds, hence the origin of the name 'Sanguisorba'.

BURR MARIGOLD (*Bidens tripartita*)

This is sometimes called Water-Agrimony, and is a strong annual growing up to two feet high, with small round yellow flowers that are slightly drooping. The leaves are three-pointed in shape. It is fairly common in Britain and can be found flowering in moist ditches in summer and autumn.

Like the Greater Burnet, this plant has astringent properties and has been used with success to check haemorrhages. An infusion is made from the whole plant and a little ginger added proves beneficial.

CALAMINT *(Calamintha officinalis)*

This is sometimes called Mountain Mint. It closely resembles Balm (Melissa officinalis) except that it is a coarser plant. It grows to about two feet in height. The purple flowers are variable in size and grow in loose whorls. They appear from July to September. The leaves are broad and oval and the plant has a mint like perfume. It is found in England and Wales, but not in Scotland, and can be seen in hedges and on banks in fairly dry places.

Calamint is used chiefly for coughs and bronchitis as it is an expectorant.

WILD CARROT *(Daucus carota)*

This plant is found all over Great Britain and Europe in the fields and open countryside. It is easy to recognise as the feathery leaves resemble our garden carrot. There is only a small root which is not edible. The flower appearing throughout the summer, is an umbel of small white flowers, and the plant often reaches a height of three feet. It smells faintly like the garden carrot which makes it easy to recognise. It is also rather hairy all over.

In the old days, the Wild Carrot was gathered extensively and made into a tea for dropsy and for cases where there was not sufficient passing of urine. Today, it is still used for bladder troubles but is more often taken in pill form. An infusion, however, can also be made from the herb.

Wild Carrot

CELANDINE *(Chelidonium majus)*

This is often known as the Greater Celandine. It grows on roadsides, and waste places, and is frequently found in Britain near houses. It reaches a height of from one to two feet. The leaves are several inches long and are green above and grey underneath. The four-petal flowers, which appear in May, are bright yellow and there are from three to six together at the top of a slender stem.

When looking for this herb, it must be remembered that it is over one foot high and belongs to the Poppy family, whereas the Lesser Celandine, known as Pilewort, is small and is one of the first to appear in spring. The latter belongs to the Buttercup family.

The Greater Celandine has a yellow bitter juice which is excellent as an application for corns and warts and is used to make ointments for this purpose. The infusion is considered helpful in cases of jaundice. Both the plant and the juice have a sharp smell.

CENTAURY *(Erythraea centaurium)*

This is sometimes called Feverwort and is found in England in the fields and woods in summer. It is a member of the Gentian family and is usually less than a foot in height. At the top of the stem there are several sprays of pink five-petal flowers bunched together, making a pleasant patch of colour.

Centaury is sometimes used in conjunction with other herbs for the treatment of jaundice. It is a useful digestive. On the continent, infusions of various members of the Gentian family are frequently used to correct digestive troubles and are kept in the home for this purpose. They are bitter and not pleasant to the taste.

CLIVERS *(Galium aparine)*

Other names for this herb are Goosegrass, Goosebill and Cleavers. Found in many parts of Britain, Europe and the world, it grows very tall and climbs freely over hedges and bushes, clinging on by little prickles like hooks.

The leaves are arranged in star-like shape round a point on the stem. A stalk grows out from the stem bearing a cluster of greenish white flowers which appear in the summer and, when flowering is over, little prickly burrs appear, which easily stick to clothing and to the fur of an animal. When picnicking in the fields, one sometimes has to work hard to remove these burrs from one's clothes as they 'cleave' a little too closely!

This herb is useful for the bladder as it is very cleansing and clearing in its effect and helps to dissolve stones.

The old herbalists recommended it as a slimming herb, no doubt due to its cleansing properties. Some spoke of it as a valuable blood purifier in spring, and it is used with other herbs for this purpose today.

COLTSFOOT *(Tussilago farfara)*

The name 'Tussilago' comes down to us from the Greek word 'tussis', meaning a cough, as throughout the centuries this plant has been considered useful for coughs and the respiratory passages. It is also called Coughwort.

The round, bright yellow glossy flowers of the Coltsfoot appear in or near the woods and on banks in March. One might mistake it at first for a Dandelion, but on close inspection it can quickly be recognised by its leaves which do not appear until the flower is over and has given place to a tuft of fluff.

The leaves and flowers of Coltsfoot are used in herbal medicines for coughs and chest complaints, together with other herbs which have similar qualities. The leaves are dried and are included in herbal smoking mixtures, so that the smoker may benefit from inhaling them.

Sufferers from acute bronchitis or asthma find relief in difficult breathing by smoking a mixture made from Coltsfoot and other herbs. Stramonium (Datura stramonium) is very beneficial in such cases.

Coltsfoot

Comfrey

COMFREY *(Symphytum officinale)*

Country names for this herb are many, but perhaps the best known are Nipbone and Knitbone. In the north of England Knitbone is sometimes the only name used for Comfrey. It grows up to three feet tall, with large hairy leaves that are smaller towards the upper part of the stem. Above the last leaf is a stalk bearing a bunch of yellow or dingy purple flowers. This herb can be seen on moist banks or at the edge of a damp meadow. It flowers in the spring and summer in England and Europe, but is not found in the extreme north of Scotland.

The root is brownish black and is used, as well as the leaves, in herbal preparations. It is excellent for all chest complaints in conjunction with other herbs. The leaves also make a fomentation which is beneficial for swellings, sprains and strains. Country people bind fresh Comfrey round a strained wrist or ankle, or make the plant into a poultice.

In the old days, herbalists used to recommend it for joining broken bones – hence the name Knitbone.

CRANESBILL *(Geranium dissectum)*

One of several varieties of the Geranium family found in England and the easiest to recognise. Another variety found in the U.S.A. is Geranium maculatum. Cranesbill grows in moist situations and reaches a height of from two to three feet. The flowers have five petals, are bluish purple, and grow in pairs. The petals soon fall off when a spray is gathered. The seeds form in a sharp pod like a bird's bill.

Gerard thought highly of this plant and recommended it to be taken internally. The root and the herb are occasionally used today for their astringent properties. Cranesbill pills, are very beneficial for strengthening the bladder and can be taken to relieve bladder weakness which is troublesome at night. They are safe and effective for children.

Cranesbill

DANDELION *(Taraxacum officinale)*

The name of this well-known wild flower comes from the French *dent-de-lion* or lion's tooth. This refers to the sharp points, like teeth, around the edge of the leaves. An older alternative botanical name is Taraxacum Dens-leonis.

The bright yellow flower, composed of narrow petals lightly packed together, frequently grows to about the size of a penny. The leaves are arranged below the flowers in a rosette very firmly rooted into the ground.

This plant is most difficult to clear from gardens and lawns where it is not wanted, as it spreads and flourishes with great persistence. It is brilliant and attractive in wild country but in cultivated ground, it has to be destroyed by the application of a weed killer.

The Dandelion root is an excellent substitute for coffee. The root is dug up, cleaned, roasted and ground, and coffee is prepared from it in the usual way. The flavour of Dandelion coffee is very pleasant and appetising. Fortunately, it can be given to anyone who is unable to digest ordinary coffee. It is most suitable for those suffering from heart troubles, high blood pressure or poor digestion. Many people have found that it also acts beneficially on the liver and kidneys. The young leaves are used in salads.

ELDER *(Sambucus nigra)*

This is the common Elder, a small tree or shrub very often seen in our hedgerows. The leaves are sharply toothed and are arranged five on the stem. The flowers appear in May and June and grow in a creamy-white whorl; the fruit is black and ripens in September. The Elder is found all over the British Isles and in parts of Europe.

An excellent treatment for the common cold and influenza is obtained from Elder flowers and Peppermint, taken as a hot drink. The bark, leaves, flowers and berries are all useful.

Dandelion

EYEBRIGHT *(Euphrasia officinalis)*

This little annual herb is found in meadows in England and is usually about six inches high. It blooms from May to September. The leaves are sharply toothed, growing opposite each other up the stalk. At the top are small whitish, two-lipped flowers, with a spot of yellow in the throat.

In Alpine regions the plant grows only one or two inches high.

The whole herb is used in herbal peparations and is combined with Golden Seal to make a lotion or ointment for the eyes. Old herbals advised that an infusion should be taken inwardly to improve the eyesight.

FENNEL *(Foeniculum vulgare)*

This is the wild Fennel which grows from two to three feet high. The plant establishes itself readily in stony, arid places, especially near the sea, and is often found on dry rocky banks. The leaves are feathery and the flowers are in yellow umbels, blooming during the summer.

The seeds (more properly called fruits) are used for the stomach, and Fennel blended with other herbs makes an excellent digestive tea. Animals readily graze from this plant where they can find it, as they seem to know instinctively that it is good for their digestion.

FEVERFEW *(Chrysanthemum Parthenium)*

This herb grows wild in the British Isles and in many parts of Europe. The flowering stems are erect and branching and about a foot high, the leaves growing alternately up a hairy stem. The flowers are like small daisies, about $\frac{1}{4}''$ across – with a yellow centre and white petals, borne on a branched head and they are seen in June and July by country roadsides and in waste places. The odour of Feverfew is very strong and pungent.

This herb has often been used, blended with others, to help to promote menstruation. The whole herb is infused and taken in liquid form.

FIGWORT *(Scrophularia nodosa)*

This is a coarse, erect perennial, growing two to three feet high. It is found all over Britain, particularly where the soil is moist. The stem is square, and the leaves are large and broadly oval. The flower is a pale greenish-purple with the upper lip more deeply coloured, and is seen all through the summer. A water species of this herb, which is generally taller and less branched, is called Water Figwort, and the flowers are dull purple. The Figwort (nodosa) is valuable as a poultice and highly effective for abscesses and skin eruptions, and can also be taken internally as an infusion.

In mediaeval times Figwort was very highly esteemed for the skin complaint known as the 'King's Evil', and was applied to the affected area by steeping the bandage in an infusion of the herb.

Other names for this herb are Rosenoble and Scrofula plant.

FUMITORY *(Fumaria officinalis)*

Fumitory is a delicate pale green annual, forming a tuft a few inches high, from which weak trailing, or sometimes climbing stems grow to a height of from one to three feet. The leaves are much divided, and generally have three lobes of various shapes. The small flowers, borne in graceful spikes, are reddish-purple. The whole plant is fern-like in appearance, and is common in waste places in England and south Scotland, disappearing in high northern latitudes.

This herb is useful as a mild aperient and for treating skin affections.

GERMANDER *(Teucrium Chamaedrys) (Chasse fievre)*

This is a perennial found on stony banks and old walls. It is not very common, and where established has often escaped from gardens. It grows to a height of six to eight inches; the leaves are oval, deeply toothed, and hairy on both sides. The flowers are in whorls and are reddish-purple. They appear in summer.

The whole herb is used as a tonic, and also for rheumatism and gout.

GOLDEN ROD _(Solidago Virga-aurea)_

This is found in woods and is common in Britain. The erect stiff stems often reach two feet in height. The leaves are oval and the flowers are crowded into heads of bright yellow blooms. They are seen in summer and autumn.

The leaves of this plant are medicinal and being diuretic are useful in kidney and bladder complaints. Also this herb has a carminative effect upon the stomach.

HEARTSEASE _(Viola tricolor)_

This is the wild Pansy. It grows with branching stems. The leaves vary in shape, sometimes being heart-shaped, and the flowers are purple, whitish and yellow, or with a mixture of these colours. The lower petals are always the broadest and are generally yellow at the base. It is abundant in Britain, especially as a weed in gardens, but it is also found in a variety of situations. It flowers right through from spring to autumn.

The herb is used in the alleviation of blood disorders, catarrhal affections and also for skin eruptions in children.

Heartsease

HOREHOUND (*Marrubium vulgare*) *White Horehound*

The thick stems of this plant grow one and a half feet high with spreading branches covered with white cottony wool. The leaves are stalked, soft and much wrinkled. The small greyish white flowers are in dense clusters in the axils of the upper leaves.

It is not very common in Britain. It flowers in summer and autumn.

The whole herb is a valuable ingredient, with other herbs, in compound teas and mixtures for relieving the chest of phlegm, and for generally easing coughs and respiratory troubles.

HORSETAIL (*Equisetum arvense*)

This herb is leafless, with erect rush-like hollow and jointed stems. Two types of stems are produced: thick fruiting stems which grow from eight to ten inches high, are followed by barren stems which are one to two feet high with slender spreading branches. There are no flowers. Abundant in Britain, Horsetail is found particularly in moist poorly-drained soil and is quite unlike any other herbs to be seen in our countryside.

This herb is astringent in action and used in medicines for kidney disorders.

LADY'S MANTLE (*Alchemilla vulgaris*)

This is a perennial which grows up to six inches high. The leaves are large, round, and borne on long stalks. The flowering stems bear a few small leaves on short green stalks. The flowers are green and produced in clusters. Distributed all over Britain, it is found in meadows and pastures, but is scarce in south-east England.

The whole herb is used as an internal astringent and has been highly esteemed for women's complaints throughout the years. It is taken as an infusion and sometimes in pill form.

LILY OF THE VALLEY (*Convallaria majalis*)

This popular garden flower is also found wild in some parts of England but it is not native to Scotland or Ireland. The broad leaves growing from the root stock taper at both ends and are from four to six inches long. The flowers are drooping, bell-shaped and pure white, with a delicate perfume. After flowering, globular red berries are produced. Lily of the Valley flowers abundantly in the woodlands in the spring.

The whole plant is used in herbal practice as a gentle heart stimulant and tonic. Unlike the Foxglove, it is non-poisonous, but has a similar beneficial action on the heart.

LOOSESTRIFE *(Lysimachia vulgaris)*

This is the common yellow Loosetrife which grows from two to three feet high. The rather large leaves are usually in whorls of three or four and are oval-shaped. The flowers are produced at the summit of the branches in bunches, each having five petals. Found frequently in England on shady banks and near streams it flowers from June to late summer.

The whole herb is used as an astringent and as a gargle for a relaxed throat.

LUNGWORT *(Pulmonaria officinalis)*

A more modern botanical name is Pulmonia longifolia. This is a small plant with spotted leaves which grow in tufts from the roots. The flowering stems, from six inches to one foot in height, have smaller leaves. The flowers are violet blue in colour and are borne in small bunches at the top of the stem. It is rare in Britain where the best areas for finding it are the woods of Hampshire and Dorset.

This herb is used in compounds with others for chest complaints, coughs and asthma. It is healing in its action and soothes inflammation.

MARJORAM, Wild *(Origanum vulgare)*

The root stock of this plant creeps and annual stems grow from one to two feet high. The leaves are oval, an inch or more long, slightly toothed, and the flowers are purple and, occasionally, white in globular compact heads. It appears on the edges of woods and on roadsides, especially in limestone districts in England, but it is rare in Scotland.

The whole herb is useful as it contains an oil, and a warm infusion of the herb helps to correct the effect of chills and promotes perspiration.

MARSHMALLOW

(*Althaea officinalis*)

This herb is a perennial, producing erect flowering stems from two to three feet high, with broad oval leaves and with flowers growing from the stem towards the top of the plant. The flowers may be described as rose colour or pinkish-mauve, and appear rather late in summer in many parts of Britain in open country, but not north of Lincolnshire.

Marshmallow is useful for coughs and bladder troubles. Healing ointments are also made from this herb, combined with Slippery Elm bark.

MEADOW - SWEET

(*Spiraea Ulmaria*) (*Also called Queen of the Meadows and Bridewort*)

This is a perennial with erect, rather stout annual stems which are smooth and reddish, The flowers are small, yellowish white, and borne in a graceful plume at the top of the stem. It is found in meadows and on the banks of streams in summer. It is very common in Britain.

The scent is sweet and an infusion is pleasant to the taste. It is incorporated in herb beers by country people.

Marshmallow

MISTLETOE *(Viscum album)*

Composed of woody succulent branches, with yellowish green leaves, the plant can grow to one or two feet in diameter attached to the branches of trees. It bears male and female flowers and from the latter the berries are produced. These are white and semi-transparent. It is found specially on the apple but very rarely on the oak. Mistletoe is common in south and west England except in Cornwall.

It is a valuable nervine, and a safe nerve medicine for children.

MOTHERWORT *(Leonurus Cardiaca) (Also called Lion's Ear)*

A tall, erect, perennial two to four feet high, its leaves are broad and deeply toothed. The flowers are borne in whorls and are pink or nearly white. This plant is found in several parts of England during the late summer and grows chiefly in waste places, hedges and roadsides.

The whole herb is used. It is especially favoured for women's complaints and is greatly esteemed as a tea for morning sickness.

MOUNTAIN FLAX *(Linum catharticum)*

A very slender annual, growing several inches high. The flowers are pure white borne on long slender stalks. It grows abundantly in Britain and will be found flowering in meadows right through the summer.

It is used in conjunction with other herbs for kidney complaints; it is also an effective laxative.

MOUSEAR *(Hieracium Pilosella)*

This is a common lawn weed. It sends out runners and the leaves are borne in rosettes close to the ground. The flowers are borne in a single head and are lemon coloured, often tinged with red on the outside. It is usually found on dry pastures, banks and roadsides, and it blooms abundantly throughout the summer.

Mousear is useful as an expectorant, and, combined with other herbs, is good for whooping cough and lung affections.

MUGWORT

(Artemisia vulgaris)

This plant has erect flowering stems two to three feet high. The leaves are coarsely toothed, green and smooth above and white underneath. The yellow flowers are borne in heads containing from twelve to twenty florets. It is found on roadsides and waste places in Britain, and blooms during late summer and autumn.

Together with Pennyroyal and Southernwood, Mugwort is used in an infusion for women's complaints.

MULLEIN

(Verbascum Thapsus)

This is an erect biennial two to four feet high, covered with soft woolly hairs. The leaves are oblong and pointed, slightly toothed, and narrowed at the base. It flowers in a dense woolly terminal spike, bright yellow in colour, and is seen on roadsides, and in waste places in summer.

An infusion of Mullein is used with other herbs in the treatment of chest complaints.

Mullein

38

NETTLES
(Stinging) *(Urtica dioica)*

The whole plant is dark green, with erect stems two to three feet high, stinging bristles and coarsely toothed leaves. Male and female flowers, greenish in colour, are borne on the same plant in clusters in the axils of the leaves. Found everywhere throughout the English countryside in waste places.

Nettles are rich in chlorophyll, and provide much of the supply used by botanical druggists. They also have valuable medicinal properties for the treatment of nettle rash (Urticaria).

PARSLEY
PIERT *(Alchemilla arvensis)*

A member of the Rose family and called by our ancestors 'Parsley Breakstone', because of its use for dissolving stones and gravel in the kidneys and bladder. The plant grows about six inches high, has large leaves with regularly toothed lobes and small green flowers borne in a loose head. Found frequently in the meadows and pastures of Britain but rather scarce in S.E. England.

This herb has proved highly beneficial in the most obstinate cases of kidney and bladder complaints. Some prefer to take it as an infusion, but it is also widely used in pill form.

Nettles

PELLITORY OF THE WALL

(*Parietaria officinalis*)

A small branching perennial one to six inches long. The leaves are lance-shaped, growing alternately up the stem. The flowers are borne in clusters in the axils of the leaves – small and green.

It is found on old walls and stony places, and flowers all the summer. It is common in Britain, but rare in the north.

It is used with other herbs to assist the action of the bladder.

Peppermint

PENNYROYAL *(Mentha Pulegium)*

This is a branching perennial that grows from nine to twelve inches high. Its leaves, much smaller than other mints, have short stalks and are slightly toothed. Its flowers, lilac in colour, bloom in late summer and are to be seen scattered generally all over England in moist places. Pennyroyal makes a warming herbal tea for the stomach, and is useful for chills particularly those experienced by women.

PEPPERMINT *(Mentha piperita)*

The Peppermint plant is a perennial. The leaves are borne on stalks, the margins of which have large teeth, smooth above and hairy underneath. The flowers are lilac in colour, borne on spikes, and seen in August. This plant appears to be of garden origin but is found wild in some localities.

Part of it used is the distilled oil of the herb for allaying flatulence and sickness and as a digestive cordial. It is now farmed in this country in large quantities for use with other medicines.

PERIWINKLE *(Vinca major)*

This is the greater Periwinkle, a trailing perennial which produces flowering stems almost a foot high. The leaves are ovate and evergreen and the single flowers are blue with five petals united to form a tube. Wherever it is found in England, it is probably a 'garden escape'. The plant rarely, if ever, produces seeds in this country.

This herb makes an excellent bitter tonic and is sometimes used to help to check haemorrhages.

PILEWORT *(Ranunculus Ficaria)*

This is the small or lesser Celandine. It is found almost everywhere in Britain. The root produces oblong or cylindrical tubers which are renewed annually. The leaves vary in size. The flowers, brilliant yellow like golden stars, appear as soon as the worst of the winter cold is over and bloom right through the spring until May.

This herb is used for the treatment of piles, internally as medicine, and outwardly as ointment.

PLANTAIN *(Plantago major)*

This perennial has very broad leaves and short leaf stalks. The flowers are on tall spikes which spring from the axils of the leaves. Most noticeable feature of the flower spike is the purple colour of the stamens. Cooling in its effect, Plantain is rarely used in herbal medicines today.

An interesting point to note about Plantains is that they have spread to every part of the world where Europeans have settled. Many coloured races call them 'White Man's Foot' for wherever the white man has gone he appears to have taken the Plantain with him.

Plantain

RAGWORT *(Senecio jacobaea)*

This belongs to the Composite family. A herb which grows to a height of two to four feet, with erect, stoutish, well-hardened leafy stems. The leaves are broken into toothed lobes. The plant is crowned throughout summer by bright yellow flower heads. It is found almost everywhere and neglected acres are, often, bright gold with this herb.

It is used with others for coughs, colds and influenza, also it has proved helpful for sciatica.

RASPBERRY *(Rubus Idaeus)*

This is a perennial, producing round stems, three to five feet, whitish with straight, slender prickles. The leaves are green above, white beneath. The flowers are white and fruits are red or yellow. It is found in woods and heaths and flowers June to August.

This has been known and used throughout the centuries as a simple and natural aid to easy childbirth.

RUPTUREWORT *(Herniaria glabra)*

The very much branched stems grow along the ground. The leaves are small and oblong, opposite and intertwined with little green flowers. It flowers all summer in southern and central counties of England and prefers sandy soil.

Its main medicinal use is for catarrh of the bladder.

SANICLE *(Sanicula europaea)*

The leaves of this plant spring from the ground on long stalks, and are deeply divided like the five fingers of the hand. The flowers are borne in compact umbels of white or pink. The plant derives its name from the Latin word 'sano' meaning 'to heal'. Common in Britain in summer, it has valuable medicinal properties and is used for purifying the blood.

SCABIOUS *(Scabiosa succisa)*

This is the Devil's Bit Scabious. The root stalk is short and ends abruptly as though bitten. The leaves are entire; the flowers purplish-blue, sometimes white, can be seen often covering large areas in meadows and pastures, from July to October. It is used for the alleviation of coughs, fevers and internal inflammation.

SCULLCAP *(Scutellaria galericulata)*

Scullcap (or skullcap) has creeping roots producing stems one or two feet high. Leaves are oval and opposite, lance shaped on short stalks. Flowers, borne in the axils of the leaves, are blue with much paler interiors. As they develop they droop slightly and turn in the same direction, giving an effect of blooming in pairs. The flowering time is from July to September.

This herb is excellent for the nerves and is one of the best that is known. It is particularly helpful in cases of nervous twitching. The variety used to-day is Scutellaria laterifolia which is imported.

SHEPHERD'S PURSE *(Capsella Bursa-pastoris)*

This annual plant has leaves of irregular shape, many of which are spread on the ground. The flowers are small and white, without honey or scent, and are succeeded by the heart-shaped or purse-shaped seed vessels from which it gets its name. It grows abundantly in Britain, flowering nearly all the year round. It is widely used in compounds for the kidneys.

SILVERWEED *(Potentilla anserina)*

This has long creeping runners which root like strawberries. The leaf sprays are silky on the upper side and shiny silvery white underneath. Flower stems are produced at the rooting joints and carry a rather large yellow flower. This herb flowers during summer and grows abundantly in Britain on roadsides and in stony or waste places. It has tonic properties and is cooling and astringent. Gypsies often put it in their boots to keep their feet cool!

SOAPWORT *(Saponaria officinalis)*

A smooth perennial, with several stout, leafy, erect stems one to two feet high. The leaves are two to three inches long, heart-shaped, with broad stalks. The large handsome pale pink flowers are produced in dense heads at the ends of stems. Although this herb may be native on coasts of Devon and Cornwall, it is probably not naturally wild in this country but may have been introduced from S. Europe. It flowers in the summer.

Soapwort is very cleansing in its action and may be described as a natural detergent. It is good for skin complaints, and beneficial in hair shampoos.

SPEEDWELL *(Veronica officinalis)*

A perennial that is common in all parts of Britain. The stems run along the ground and take root, growing erect for a few inches. The leaves are oval or slightly round and coarsely toothed. The flowers are in pale blue or lilac sprays. Found on banks and dry pastures, it blooms throughout the summer.

Speedwell is a useful herb for treating skin troubles, also coughs, catarrh and women's complaints.

Silverweed

ST. JOHN'S WORT *(Hypericum perforatum)*

This is an attractive creeping plant. The flowers are about an inch in diameter, and yellow marked with black dots and lines, and grow in clusters with a multitude of stamens. It is found frequently in copses and hedgebanks as far north as Sunderland, flowering from July to September.

It is used for coughs and respiratory troubles and has also been found beneficial for urinary disorders.

TANSY *(Tanacetum vulgare)*

This is a perennial with a creeping root stock, from which grow beautiful broad feathery leaves and flowering stems. The leaves are deeply divided and toothed. The flower head is golden yellow with a bunch of bright flowers. It can be seen from July to September in most parts of Britain.

Tansy has been found useful for expelling worms in children. Other uses claimed for it include a tonic to help in women's complaints.

Tansy

THYME WILD

(Thymus serpyllum)

The stems of this plant creep, and the leaves are small, stalked, egg-shaped, and often turned under. The flowers are rosy-purple and borne in whorls; they produce a lot of honey and the whole plant is delightfully fragrant. It grows in high pastures and is close-cropped by sheep. It is found from June to September.

The action of this herb is anti-spasmodic and carminative.

UVA URSI *(Arctostaphylos uva-ursi)*

The procumbent stems are massed together with a large number of evergreen oblong leaves, which are about one inch long. Flowers are followed by bright red shining berries. It is found on dry heathy or rocky hills in Scotland, northern England and Ireland.

The leaves of this shrub are used with other herbs for the treatment of gravel, kidney and bladder disorders.

VALERIAN *(Valeriana officinalis)*

The stems grow from two to five feet high, with broad panicles of pink or white flowers. The leaves are rather narrow and notched on both sides. The flowers are seen from June to August by the side of streams and in other watery situations. It is not very common but where found is abundant.

Valerian is a most valuable nervine and anti-spasmodic herb. As its taste and odour are very strong and pungent, it is usually better taken in pill form.

VERVAIN *(Verbena officinalis)*

The stems are square and grow to a height of one to two feet, branching at the top. The leaves are oblong and cut into lobes. It flowers from July to September in terminal spikes coloured lilac or pinkish blue.

This herb is useful in nervous conditions and is advised where headache is present.

VIOLET *(Viola odorata)*

This is called the Sweet Violet. The leaves are broadly heart-shaped and the flowers blue, reddish purple or white. It grows by means of runners and is found on sheltered banks. It is truly wild in southern and eastern England, and possibly eastern Ireland, but is naturalised in many other parts.

Violet is an antiseptic. In the old days, the herb was considered beneficial for internal growths, taken as an infusion, and for external growths as a poultice or fomentation.

WOODRUFF *(Asperula odorata)*

The root of this plant creeps underground, producing slender erect stems about one foot high. The smooth leaves are borne in whorls. It blooms in May and June, the flowers being very small and ivory white, followed by tiny fruits covered with bristles. It is found in close patches and is plentiful in beechwoods.

This herb is good for the liver and stomach.

WOOD SAGE *(Teucrium Scorodonia)*

Before the plant flowers, it could easily be mistaken for ordinary Sage. Runners creep underground and the tufted stems grow about two feet high. The leaves are soft, wrinkled and downy, and widely spaced in pairs. The yellow flowers are borne in sprays and bell-shaped with purple stamens. It is seen in woods and hedge banks from July to September.

This herb is a tonic and has a warming effect. Among other herbs it is helpful for women's complaints in the case of a chill.

WORMWOOD *(Artemisia Absinthium)*

The stems grow from one to three feet high, with leaves which are silky on both sides and dotted. They are cut into lobes. The flower heads, coloured dingy yellow, are numerous, drooping, and globular. In Britain, this plant is often found near to the sea during August and September, and also inland in certain localised areas.

Wormwood aids poor digestion and debility and is effective in dispelling worms.

YARROW or MILFOIL *(Achillea millefolium)*

This is a creeping plant. The leaves are divided into a large number of segments, giving a feathery effect. The flower stems are about one foot high and the flowers small, white and daisy-like. One of our commonest weeds, it can be seen in pastures and on commons all over the country during August.

A useful herb for colds and influenza and beneficial as a hot drink in cases of high temperature.

HERBS IN THE GARDEN

Throughout the centuries herb gardens have been part of our history. It has often been a struggle to keep alive the art of herb gardening, and we read that in the dark ages, after the break up of the Roman Empire, only the monasteries managed to preserve and maintain their gardens. Ordinary people just managed to keep and tend small plots with herb plants for medicines and food, and were often desperately dependent on these. Doctors were few and far between and, during the restless years of continual warfare, the housewife had to rely on what she could grow or gather for the relief of family sickness, and for a little extra nourishment for the home.

The monastery gardens must have been a picture of neatness and shapeliness, being set out with formal beds, each containing a separate herb ready for use when the pilgrims came from far and wide bringing their sick ones for treatment. Few actual plans of these early herb gardens have been preserved, the earliest being that of the monastery at Canterbury which is dated A.D. 1165.

After the dissolution of the monasteries, many of these valuable and beautifully cultivated gardens disappeared, and naturally people began to establish gardens of their own to supply their needs. Large manor houses all had their herb gardens and the women of the household superintended them and were skilled in the uses of the plants. The lady of the manor and her daughters prepared medicines, vinegars and wines, poultices and lotions, perfumes, pomanders and pot-pourri, and it was considered most important that every young girl should be thoroughly trained in these duties. One can picture the ladies of the house, in their charming dresses, gathering their flowers and leaves, with all the time in the world to give to the pleasant task of preparing a tisane or tying up the bunches of kitchen herbs to dry. In the rush and bustle of life today, the housewife scarcely has a moment of leisure, and we have to be content with the simplest and quickest ways of getting things done.

Herbs played a tremendous part in the lives of the first Elizabethans. Throughout Shakespeare's plays these plants are constantly mentioned, sometimes in serious vein and sometimes in pure fun. In the play 'All's well that ends well' Helena cures the illness of the King with the herbal prescription left to her by her father, who is named by Shakespeare 'Gerard de Narbon'. Is this a hint that Shakespeare visited the garden in Holborn of the great Gerard himself? Helena pleads to be allowed to try her simple remedy for the King's sickness, saying:

> 'He that of greatest works is finisher,
> Oft does them by the weakest minister'.

The King is restored to health and so 'all ends well'.

Many references to culinary herbs occur in the gay scenes in Shakespeare's plays. In 'The Taming of the Shrew', a servant urges the young lover, Lucentio, to run to church and marry his Bianca before her father has time to find out. 'I cannot tarry . . . .' he says. 'I knew a wench married in an afternoon as she went to the garden for parsley to stuff a rabbit; and so may you, sir'.

Physic gardens were established as time went on to enable students to study the medicinal plants and have them at hand for use. In 1673, the Apothecaries' Company purchased about $3\frac{1}{2}$ acres of land in Chelsea and the famous Chelsea Physic Garden was laid out and used for the serious study of botanical medicine.

The years have brought many changes in medical practice, and the necessity for large gardens, such as were seen in the past, has gradually declined. Herbs today are farmed and harvested in large quantities and imported from all parts of the world. The walled garden, with its trim beds of 'simples', has disappeared and often only traces can be seen in grounds of our stately homes. However, the interest of many people in growing their own herbs is steadily being revived, and a few suggestions for the small plot may be welcomed by some readers of these pages.

First of all, the culinary herbs should be grown as near the back door as possible. When we need a bunch of Parsley to garnish a dish or chop for sauce, it is too far to have to walk to the extra allotment at the top of the road! The man of the house will remember to bring home a marrow but he will not, as a rule, remember the items for the stuffing.

Secondly, do not attempt to raise too many varieties or run the risk of being worried by weeds. The simpler the plan the better, and a few plants attractively displayed and nicely kept are more worth having than a mass of growth that has got out of control.

The plants suggested in the following list are easy to grow and are not fussy about their soil or aspect. Some details of their uses and history are given in the hope that they may be of interest.

ANGELICA (*Angelica archangelica*) Biennial, raised from seed. Grows very tall and should be sown at the back of any group. An old legend says it was revealed by an angel to cure the plague. The stems are used for candying.

BALM (*Melissa officinalis*) Perennial. Raised from seed. The leaves have a lovely lemon fragrance and make a refreshing tea. Bees are particularly attracted to this plant because of the large amount of honey contained in the flowers.

BASIL (*Sweet*) (*Ocymum basilicum*) Raised from seed, this half hardy annual should be planted towards the end of May. It seeds itself readily. Allow plenty of room and give a sunny position. The leaves are used to flavour soups and stews.

BAY (*Laurus nobilis*) This is the shrub from which Bay leaves are gathered for flavouring all the year round. Their taste is so penetrating that often only half a leaf is sufficient to make gravy or sauce most delicious. The leaves dried and packeted retain their quality well for a long time.

BERGAMOT (*Monarda didyma*) These should be obtained as rooted cuttings. The shades of the flowers are in a delicate range of pink and rose. The perfume is refreshing. The Flora Historica (1824) records that 'Many people prefer this tea to the tea of China'. These plants require attention to keep away weeds, otherwise they become rather weak.

BORAGE (*Borago officinalis*) This is a hardy annual to raise from seed and sown in the spring. Thin out well to allow plenty of space. Sprigs of Borage put in fruit drinks or wine-cup are a wonderful addition to the flavour and are most cooling. A great favourite with the herbalists of old time. Gerard said in his 'Herbal' of 1597, 'I, Borage, bring alwaies courage', and goes on to say it is used 'for the comfort of the heart, for the driving away of sorrow . . . the leaves and floures put into wine make men glad and merry and drive away all sadness and melancholy'.

CARAWAY (*Carum carvi*) Caraway seeds are well known for their flavour in cakes. This plant is a biennial with foliage rather like the Carrot and it can be raised from seed. Sow in September to obtain the seed the following year. Plant out a foot apart in the spring.

CATMINT (*Nepeta grandiflora*) The delicate blue sprays of this flower are beautiful for indoor arrangements and they also attract bees to the garden. Cats love it and bite the young shoots, so it is advisable to cover with wire-netting until well grown. It is a perennial and can be raised from seed or cuttings.

CHAMOMILE (*Anthemis nobilis*) Chamomile lawns are becoming very popular, as they were in the days of famous herb gardens. It must be remembered that these lawns need a lot of weeding until well established, so a small path between herb borders is probably sufficient to undertake. Sow the seeds in a box and plant the seedlings six inches apart. These lawns are fragrant and delightful to walk upon. Chamomile is invaluable as a medicinal herb and is included in many herb remedies as a tonic and nerve sedative.

CHIVES (*Allium Schoenoprasum*) A well-known culinary plant. It can be raised from seed and later clumps can be divided to increase the stock. The flowers are dainty, but if the herb is wanted for chopping the young shoots (delicious in soups and salads) it should be kept well shorn down to promote continuous new growth. Chives belong to the onion family, and when serving with salad should be placed in a separate dish in case the flavour is not liked by some.

DILL (*Anethum graveolens*) A pretty, feathery annual herb which grows to about two feet in height. Sow the seed in spring and thin out, or transplant. This is the herb which for centuries has provided Dill water for soothing infants suffering from any digestive discomforts. Herbalists today use it for this purpose in the form of infant soothing jelly, a more convenient form of dosage than the water.

FENNEL (*Foeniculum officinalis*) A perennial with beautiful fern-like foliage, which can be cut frequently for making Fennel sauce and for flavourings. It is excellent with fish. This herb can be raised from seed in the spring.

GARLIC (*Allium sativum*) Plant cloves of this herb in the autumn about two inches deep. The following summer harvest them as soon as the foliage has faded and tie in bunches and hang in a dry frostproof place. Garlic is excellent for the health and acts as a kind of internal antiseptic. Capsules made from this herb help to keep the body clear from infections and are tonic in their effect. Breeders of pedigree dogs give garlic pills to their animals, from time to time, and find this helps against disease.

LAVENDER (*Lavendula spica*) This beautiful herb is not always easy to establish. It is best to take cuttings in spring and strike them in sandy soil. A position in full sun is advisable. The fragrance of Lavender is refreshing for invalids and is pleasant anywhere in the house, especially in the linen cupboard. For making Lavender sachets, take the flowers from the stem and dry them before they come out fully. After flowering time, cut all stems down to an inch or two above the base. Young plants do not stand a severe winter.

There are many interesting stories in the life history of this herb. For example, the Greeks call spike Lavender 'Nard', and it was referred to in St. Mark's Gospel as Spikenard from which the precious ointment was made.

LOVAGE (*Levisticum officinalis*) The leaves of this plant are handsome and shiny. It is a perennial, growing sometimes several feet high. Raise from seed or from root division in autumn. The strong aroma of this herb makes it a suitable addition to a scented garden. The leaves may be added to soups and stews. In olden times Lovage Cordial was a favourite in the country.

MARJORAM Sweet (*Origanum Marjorana*) The scent of this plant is quite different from the other kitchen herbs, and it makes a unique contribution to stuffings. Treat this as a half hardy annual, sowing the seed in late May. It was one of the herbs used in mediaeval times to strew the floors of houses to sweeten the air.

MINTS (*Mentha species*) There are many varieties of this favourite herb. One most often found in gardens is Mentha spicata. This is propagated by division of the roots in spring and autumn. It likes part shade and will fill an otherwise unprofitable corner of the garden. Apart from its use in cookery, Mint tea is excellent as a tonic and a digestive. Gerard wrote, 'The smelle rejoiceth the heart of man, for which cause it is strewn in places where feasts and banquets are made'.

It spreads rapidly and needs control as it will trespass in the space reserved for other plants. A rare and lovely variety is Eau-de-Cologne Mint, which when crushed in the hand resembles in its aroma the famous perfume.

PARSLEY (*Petroselinum hortensis*) Parsley is excellent for improving the health. Sow the seed in March and again in July or August for a winter supply. It is often very slow to germinate and may not appear for some weeks. Parsley is difficult to dry at home, so it is wise to make sure of sowing for the winter and keeping packeted supplies in the store cupboard.

ROSEMARY (*Rosmarinus officinalis*) This may be regarded as the Queen of the herb garden. Obtain a strong plant and set in a sunny position, fairly sheltered from frost and cold winds. The charming blue-mauve flowers against the dark foliage are a fine sight. The leaves chopped finely are delicious added to fried fillets of veal, also as a flavouring in salads, soups and stews. Use sparingly as it is very pungent. Herbal hair tonics and shampoos are made from this plant.

RUE (*Ruta graveolens*) This plant may be raised from seeds or cuttings. It does best in soil which contains some lime. Succeeds equally well in sun or part shade. Used for seasoning and is said to help the appetite.

SAGE (*Salvia officinalis*) Does best on a fairly light soil but will not always stand a severe winter. It is not difficult, however, to grow. May be raised from seeds or cuttings. Stuffings which contain Sage are excellent with any rich or greasy foods as Sage aids digestion, hence the age-long custom of using Sage stuffings with such dishes as duck, goose and pork.

SAVORY Summer (*Satureia hortensis*) This is an annual and can be raised from seed, the later sowings are more likely to do well. It has a strong aromatic flavour. On the continent, Savory is used to put in the water when boiling broad beans, just as we use Mint with peas.

SAVORY Winter (*Satureia montana*) This evergreen shrub can be raised either from seeds or cuttings. A sunny position is the best. Winter Savory was a favourite, in Tudor times, for the short evergreen hedges in knot gardens.

Country people still prize Savory for the relief it gives when rubbed on wasp or bee stings.

TARRAGON (*Artemisia dracunculus*) This is a perennial, growing up to four feet in height. Increase by dividing and replanting in spring or autumn. It succeeds best in rather poor soil.

THYME (*Thymus species*) The best known of the Thymes is the garden variety, Thymus vulgaris. It can be raised from seeds or from cuttings taken in spring. Choose a position in full sun. Thyme is a favourite bee plant. Its scent is delightful and refreshing. In the kitchen, it is valuable for stuffings.

Herbal smoking mixture contain this herb, as it helps to keep the head clear and is fragrant. In the old days it was one of the herbs used to spread on the floor at banquets and ceremonial occasions to freshen the air.

NOTES FOR THE BEGINNER GARDENER

Some gardening terms explained

ANNUALS Plants which can be raised from seeds sown out-of-doors during the spring to bloom, seed, and finish their life cycle in the same year.

HALF HARDY ANNUALS These have the same annual life cycle but are tender and susceptible to frost. They must not be sown out-of-doors, or planted out, until the fear of frost is past. Many gardeners raise them in boxes and wait for suitable weather to set out.

BIENNIALS Normally these do not bloom the same year as the seeds are sown. They bloom and finish their life cycle the following year.

PERENNIALS The plant continues to appear from the root year after year. Occasionally it is advisable to lift and divide the roots and replant.

HOME MADE WINES

The popularity of wine drinking has increased considerably in this country during recent years. Unfortunately the cost of good commercial wines is a serious handicap to many who would enjoy this pleasant addition to the table.

The old country craft of making wine at home is the answer, and is a very fascinating hobby. First-class wine can be produced for less than 2/– per bottle, according to cost of the ingredients used.

Process and utensils are simple, rules are few, and there is nothing complicated about the three stages of converting liquid into wine.

The most important rule is never 'ferment' in anything other than earthenware or glass. Ordinary kitchen pans or saucepans may used for boiling, and of course, all equipment must be quite clean before use.

EQUIPMENT NEEDED

An earthenware crock to hold about $1\frac{1}{2}$ gallons of liquid; this will provide one gallon of wine as naturally space is required for the fruit, sugar, etc. The old-fashioned bread panshon with a wide top is good for this or, better still, an earthenware egg-preserving crock, as these come with a fitted lid. Good hardware stores will supply these and, incidentally, when not in use for wine it will provide cool storage for butter and milk in hot weather. Also required are butter muslin for straining, a large wooden spoon, a glass jar to hold one gallon, bottles, clean corks, and a length of rubber tubing for siphoning off the wine when bottling.

This is all the basic equipment necessary.

At first it is best to follow a proved recipe. Later on it is fun to make up your own recipe and experiment to suit individual taste and preference.

Failures are very rare as a too dry wine can always be mixed with wine that is too sweet, and the result will be well worth drinking.

TWO POINTS TO REMEMBER

(1) Cover the fermenting wine to exclude microbes present in the air which can cause wine to 'vinegar'. When filling the glass jar, use a cork which can easily be replaced if it pops out or, better still, use a fermentation trap. Cost is only approximately 3/6d. and they are designed to allow the gas to escape without permitting the entry of air.

(2) Wine will not 'ferment' if in a cold place. Add the yeast when liquid is about blood heat, or new milk warm, and keep in a normal home temperature of about 60°. If too cold, wine does not spoil, it simply stands still and will again commence fermenting if moved to a warmer spot.

Flowers, fruit and leaves, require only soaking in boiling water for 24 hours, then squeezing and straining before adding sugar, yeast, etc., according to the recipe.

YEAST

Very good wines are possible with ordinary Bakers' Yeast which must, of course, be fresh. Very useful indeed is dried live yeast which can be obtained from Health Stores. This will keep in the cupboard for months until required. It has twice the strength of fresh yeast so use half the recipe quantity.

Yeast Nutriment can be obtained from suppliers of wine making equipment, and is added to boost fermentation. Actually, it is not strictly necessary, the juice and thin rind of two lemons per gallon has much the same effect.

Baker's Yeast is best added by spreading on a lightly toasted thick slice of bread which then floats on the surface of the wine.

Dried Yeast Prepare a 'Starter' by mixing yeast with a little of the cool liquid; it will quickly begin to ferment and then stir well into the wine.

Fermentation is easily recognised by the bubbling action of the surface of the wine and in the vigorous stage a low 'hissing' rather like a hive of contented bees.

Other 'wrinkles' are quickly acquired. One ounce of root Ginger (well bruised), Mustard seed, whole Cloves, etc. any of these added to one gallon of wine create that warming 'tingle' or heat. The flavour will be noticeable for two or three months but this disappears and the warmth remains.

In country districts where Cowslips are available the wine may be made in the same manner as Elderflower

Some wine-makers use special wine yeasts. This involves sterilising containers and the use of chemicals to exclude natural yeast which is present on all fruits. Simple methods are more often preferred.

Further hints are: always use raisins with seeds, as these impart tannin to the wine.

White sugar is best. Brown sugar is sometimes useful to impart colour.

The addition of brandy fortifies a wine without affecting flavour, a quarter bottle to a gallon of wine, but is not essential.

Blackberry Wine does not develop a lot of strength and is helped by one glass of rum to each gallon.

Always pick flowers off and do not include thick green stems. This also applies to Parsley or the wine may be bitter. Orange and Lemon rind should be thinly peeled.

Always exclude air and fill bottles and jars to within one inch of the top.

Honey may be used in place of sugar, but requires care; too much will 'flavour' a delicate Flower wine and create a strong spirit content which is too 'heady'.

Barley wine is very potent, although mild in taste, and should be used with care and definitely not taken before driving.

CLEARING WINES

Most wines clear easily and naturally. Vegetable wines take longer than Flower wines. The fermentation goes on quietly for months, the wine gaining in strength and flavour, and it is not possible to clear wine while this is taking place. Siphoning off into another jar or moving to a warmer position will often speed up fermentation.

A fruit wine may appear to remain 'cloudy' despite all efforts. This is due to an excess of pectin in the fruit, and may be removed by adding to one gallon the shells of two fresh eggs. Isinglass can also be used but is not easy for small quantities.

TONIC WINES

Wines prepared from some herbs and vegetables are beneficial.

Elderberry Wine taken hot with honey is a country remedy for colds.

Dandelion Wine is excellent to assist the liver and digestive functions.

Beetroot Wine is recommended as a tonic for the blood and anaemic conditions.

Blackcurrant Wine provides vitamins.

Hops. Wines containing hops are good for stimulating the appetite.

Parsley Wine is quick to mature and a good tonic for the kidneys.

RECIPES

BEETROOT WINE *4 lbs. beetroot, 1 gallon water, 4 lbs. sugar, 1 lb. wheat, 1 oz. yeast.*

Method Boil beetroot until tender, strain the liquid and add sugar and stir until dissolved.

When cool, add the wheat and yeast floating on toast.

Ferment for 14 days, then strain and bottle.

      N.B. The beetroot can be covered with vinegar after boiling and used as food.

CARROT WINE *6 lbs. carrots, 3½ lbs. sugar, 2 oranges, 2 lemons, 1 oz. yeast on toast.*

Method Method as for Mangold Wine.

Ferment for 14 days, strain and bottle, then keep for 6 months or longer.

DANDELION WINE *1 gallon dandelion flower petals, 1 gallon boiling water, 1 orange, 1 lemon, 3 lbs. sugar, 1 oz. of ginger root (well bruised), ½ oz. yeast on toast.*

Method Wash dandelion flowers, and cover with boiling water and stand 3 days, stirring often and squeezing the flowers out.

Strain and put liquid into crock, add thin rind of lemon and orange, sugar and ginger, and the orange and lemon sliced. Boil for 30 minutes then allow to cool.

Spread yeast on toast and float in the liquid.

Ferment for 6 days then transfer to 1 gallon jar until clear.

ELDERBERRY WINE (Port-like) *1 gallon water, 2 quarts elderberries, 3 lbs. sugar, ½ lb. raisins, 1 oz. yeast.*

Method Strip berries off the stalks, boil with the water for 15 minutes, then strain

Add sugar and raisins to the liquid and simmer gently for 20 minutes.

Allow to cool, add yeast (spread on toast), cover and leave to ferment for 14 days. Strain and bottle.

Cork lightly, then firmly after fermentation has ceased.

Keep for 12 months.

ELDERFLOWER WINE *1 pint elder flowers, 1 gallon water, 3½ lbs. sugar, ½ lb. raisins, 3 sliced lemons, ½ oz. yeast.*

Method Pick flowers off thick stems, put into pan and simmer for 15 minutes.

Put into bowl, and add sugar and raisins and sliced lemons, stir sugar away and when lukewarm sprinkle yeast on top.

Ferment for 14 days, then strain carefully into jar, being careful not to disturb the sediment in the bottom, then bottle.

      This is very like champagne.

HAWTHORN WINE

½ gallon hawthorn blossom (May-flower), 1 gallon water, 3 lbs. sugar, 1 lb. wheat, ½ lb. raisins, 1 oz. yeast on toast.

Method Put May blossom in crock.
Boil sugar and water together and pour it over the blossoms.
When lukewarm add chopped raisins, wheat, and yeast.
Leave to ferment 16 days, then strain and bottle.

MANGOLD WINE

(Very potent) 1 gallon of mangolds, i.e. 4-6 lbs., 1 gallon of water, 3 lbs. sugar, 1 oz. yeast, ½ oz. dried hops.

Method Wash mangolds and pare off the rough roots.
Cut up and boil until tender, then strain.
Put sugar into liquid and stir until dissolved.
Put the hops in and when lukewarm add yeast on toast.
Leave 21 days to ferment, then strain and bottle.
(Made in March) (A good strong wine)

PARSNIP WINE

4 lbs. parsnips, 1 gallon water, 3½ lbs. sugar, 1 oz. lump ginger, ½ lb. wheat, 1 lemon, ½ lb. raisins with seeds, 1 oz. yeast on toast, 1 oz. hop flowers (dried).

Method Clean parsnips, cut up and boil until tender, then strain.
Add sugar, ginger and hops, to the liquid and boil for five minutes.
Turn liquid into fermenting crock, add juice and rind of lemon and the chopped raisins. Allow to cool before adding the yeast (spread on toast) and the wheat.
Ferment for 14 days then skim and bottle—keep for 9 months to 1 year.

POTATO WINE

1 lb. wheat, 1 lb. raisins, 1 lb. potatoes, 4 lbs. sugar, 1 gallon water, 1 oz. yeast.

Method Put wheat, chopped raisins, and clean chopped potatoes into crock, add sugar and cover with warm water.
Add yeast and leave to ferment for 3 weeks, then strain and bottle.
   Simple to make and produces a fine golden wine.

WHEAT WINE

1 lb. wheat, 2 lbs. sultanas (chopped), 1 lb. old potatoes (chopped finely), 4 lbs. sugar, 1 oz. yeast, 1 gallon hot water, 2 grapefruits.

Method Put wheat, sultanas, potatoes, sugar, juice and rind of grapefruit into a bowl.
Pour on hot water and stir until sugar is dissolved.
When it cools to lukewarm, sprinkle the yeast in and leave to ferment 21 days.
Then strain into gallon jar to clear.
   Good in six months.

HERBS AND THE ANIMALS

Animals seem to know by instinct which herbs are beneficial to them and the grazing animal will select certain herb plants as a change from grass. The use of weed killers in recent years has deprived the animals of many wild plants. Among those which they miss are Sweet Clover, Sheeps Parsley, Kidney Vetch, Yarrow and Burnet. Some owners of grazing land have made herb strip sowings and the animals have benefited.

Herbs can often help our pets. A good tonic for a dog is a teaspoon of powdered seaweed sprinkled over his food twice a week. Garlic is also good and can be given in capsule form, or the corm chopped up finely and mixed in food. Garlic protects against disease and worms and helps to fight off colds. Owners of hens report that this herb is good for birds when suffering from colds. They recommend slipping a capsule down the bird's throat night and morning, keeping her warm and dry and giving mash, plenty of water and green food. For a cat's stuffy cold Friars Balsam is recommended. Put the cat in a closed-in basket and raise the basket on two chairs leaving a gap underneath. Put the jug of steaming Friars Balsam under the gap covering with a towel and leaving for about twenty minutes. Take the cat out but keep very warm after treatment

and do not allow it out of doors. Raise the food dishes a few inches from the ground. Small doses of herbal mixture of Elderflower, Peppermint and Composition Essence will help.

Raspberry leaves in tablet form can be given to our domestic animals from the third week of pregnancy, the dose being one tablet a day for small cats and dogs and two a day for larger animals. Slippery Elm Food is also excellent for the nursing mother or any delicate animal. When old dogs are restless at night give Slippery Elm Food last thing, and, if still unsettled, a Scullcap pill is good.

For a dog's rheumatism give a daily dose of an infusion of Parsley leaves. Home made biscuits containing Molasses are helpful. For external massage an infusion of equal parts of Seaweed and Thyme rubbed on to the painful limb will ease the pain. Pyrethrum powder is good for any trouble with fleas. Rub this well into the animal's coat or sprinkle under the bird's feathers after it has roosted for the night. Nature's remedies, in most cases, are best for our animals and birds.

Finally, notify the Veterinary Surgeon the moment you notice any sign of ill health or discomfort, so that the trouble may be taken in time.

RECOLLECTIONS
OF A HERB SPECIALIST

For many years it was my special duty to give advice to many thousands of people on the use of herbs as remedies and for all kinds of purposes.

I suppose I must have been about ten years of age when first I became interested in plants, shrubs and trees. My father was a keen botanist and loved everything he saw in the botanical world. One of his favourite haunts was Epping Forest, where he used to take my brother and myself as often as occasion would permit. There he would impart to us all the knowledge he possessed. He taught us the names of the plants, trees, their structural differences, their habits, and where he knew them, their medicinal virtues. Apart from their Latin names, he was particularly charmed with the common names by which so many of them were known. I think, indeed I am sure, my father often perceived the look of wonderment in my face as I eagerly took in all the wonders of nature.

As I grew up, these peregrinations along forest paths, in the woods and glades, around marshy and boggy places, filled me with wonder and awe. I was fascinated as I tried to absorb all I was taught. My kindly father encouraged me in my thirst for knowledge, and I am deeply indebted to him for his patience in answering all my questions during the formative years of my youth. His answers were always simple and to the point. Sometimes he would reply, 'I just don't know, my boy'. He would say to me: 'Knowledge is a great accomplishment. Learn all you can and endeavour to arrive at the truth'.

Those wanderings through the forest, along country lanes, over fields and by the hedgerows, added to my interest and love of all I beheld.

My very dear parents taught us when we were young that everything in creation had a useful purpose. Boy as I was, I couldn't see this at the time. Indeed, I must confess there were some things for which I could see no purpose at all in creation. I suppose this view of mine was due to the fact that I feared and was frightened of some forms of animal and insect life. With plants and vegetable life, however, I had no fears, and loved them all. So far as these were concerned, I continued to think of them and study them, giving up many other interests to do so. These must indeed have a useful purpose. I thought, and one day I came to the decision that I would discover what uses they could serve. This resolution of mine was hastened one day when I had been walking along the banks of the river Lea on a late June day studying certain plant life. It was necessary that I cross into a field by means of a stile. Being young and agile, I endeavoured to jump this entry into the next field, as many another boy would do. I failed to clear it, and caught my foot on the top rung and fell heavily to the ground. The result was a badly grazed and bruised knee which pained me considerably. A man, who had been fishing, saw what had happened and cleaned my knee. From the river bank he cut two or three broad leaves from the common Comfrey growing there, applied them to the damaged parts, and tied them into position to prevent the leaves from shifting. This treatment really worked wonders, quickly dispersing the swelling, and all pain by the next morning.

This incident spurred me on in my studies and knowledge of the remedial

Hazel

virtues of many herbs and was retained by me for use in the future. Here was a field of activity in which I could surely be of use in the years before me; and so it turned out to be.

Knowledge that certain herbs could be administered in the effective treatment of everyday common ailments certainly did not satisfy me. I wanted to know why and how they did their curative work in healing ailments. During mankind's earliest days the usefulness of herbs in the treatment of disease must have depended on the practice or principle of trial and error, and the knowledge of success or failure then handed down from generation to generation.

I scanned all the old Herbals and writers on the subject of herbs and their uses that I could find.

At last I found the answer to my enquiring mind. Coming to our own times we know that chemical research has established the fact that plants contain certain medicinal principles and salts which have their curative action. These have all been proved in the treatment of disease, so that we no longer have to rely upon mere tradition for their success in illness.

With my increased knowledge and experience, and a burning desire to be useful to my fellow creatures, I ultimately found myself in a position where my knowledge could find a real outlet.

For well over thirty years, I was able to advise and help many sufferers from common complaints.

My recollections have been both grave and gay during those years, and very rewarding, too.

During the nineteen twenties, one of my greatest rewards was when I was approached by a considerable number of bus drivers, all of whom informed me they were suffering from gastritis, in varying degrees of discomfort. Could I possibly do anything to assist them? Nothing they had tried proved satisfactory. 'Yes', I said, 'I cannot guarantee a cure, but I am confident you can be much relieved'. I thought much about their trouble, and advised certain herbs and Slippery Elm food, the former three times daily after meals, and the latter twice daily. The result was most satisfactory, and within a few days, most of them were back at work free from discomfort.

Letters came in to me daily from every part of the world. They came from remote islands, from R.A.F. camps in distant lands, from ships at sea, from lonely mission stations and from many British folks living in parts of the Commonwealth who told me of their life and conditions so far from 'home'. Needless to say the foreign stamps gave much pleasure to many of my young friends who were collectors!

Sometimes I have treated animals and birds not, I confess, always with the same confidence as when dealing with human beings. Once a little boy came to me and said, 'Can you treat parrots, guvnor?' 'I'm not sure'. I answered. 'My dad's got one, an' he's lost his voice; he don't talk now. Dad says, 'Can you give him some herbs to give him his voice back?' This was indeed a poser for me, for I had never treated a parrot before this. Not without some doubts and fears, the bird was given a teaspoonful of the decoction of Raspberry leaves and Blackberry leaves with a few drops of whisky added. This was given every four hours. The result was excellent and in four days 'Nobby', the grey parrot, was well and talking normally. This was a great relief to me!

The late Gipsy Petulengro and I had many a talk together and we often exchanged experiences. I found him a very interesting personality and often supplied him with herbs he could not himself obtain, which pleased him considerably. He was sincere at all times, and like myself unshakeable in his faith in herb treatment for common ailments. I was indeed sorry to learn of his death, for I believe he did a great deal for his own people through herbs.

The present day use of herbs is thought by a few people to be lessening, but my own experience shows that this is not so. Many people are tired of the purely chemical treatment in vogue today, and are returning in large numbers to the simple herb treatment used so much by our grandparents. I am often asked in my retirement to advise remedies and I do so where I can and opportunity occurs.

There are literally hundreds of herbs, the medicinal virtues of which are well-known, and which are used in thousands of homes today. Some of my own personal favourites are Chamomile, Vervain, Valerian, and Scullcap for nerve affections, Buckbean, Yarrow, Celery seed and Garlic for that scourge of today: rheumatism. I advise Marshmallow, Comfrey, Figwort, Clivers and Selfheal for wounds. Such herbs as Elecampane, Horehound, Comfrey, Liquorice, Hyssop, Coltsfoot and Garlic for coughs and chest affections. For digestive troubles nature provides Centaury, Fennel seeds, Coriander seeds, Slippery Elm, Chamomile, Calumba root and many others. For a very good tonic Poplar bark (White) as well as Hops, Chamomile and Centaury can be thoroughly recommended. Much use is made of Burdock, Sanicle, Buckbean and Stinging Nettles for skin and blood disorders, while Clivers, Wild Carrot, Uva ursi, and Dandelion are valuable for kidney and bladder complaints.

These are only a very few of the herbs for common ailments used by me. For those who read these recollections of mine, please remember that Herbal treatment will not cure everything, but I have had the joy and satisfaction of knowing that I have helped many a sufferer to normal and happy health again. Herbalism is today an exact science and also the oldest form of medicine used by man.

In conclusion, I have given but a very few of the many experiences and varied recollections I have of my work with herbs. Suffice it to say I enjoyed it all, and am happy to know that my knowledge of plants and their uses enabled me to put them to good use. From my Devon home of retirement, I can still take my walks into the country lanes, woods and fields, realising something of the wonders of creation and its purpose and still thirsting for knowledge, and if I am still affectionately addressed by some as the 'Doc' – well! I don't mind that at all.

S. F. M.